When he was a young n
shepherd, David was told
someone very special one da

How many sheep is David
find them. Where is David'

What was David to
become one day? Rub
to find out. >>>

Hidden in the pages
of this book are ten
shepherds' crooks. Find
them!

David lived in Israel and the Philistines were at war with his country. One of the Philistine warriors was a great giant called Goliath. He called to the Israelites to come and fight him.

Goliath was a giant! Rub below to find out how big he was.

Which two helmets are exactly the same?

The Israelites were all terrified of Goliath because he was such a fierce and strong fighter.

Which is the biggest thing in these six pictures? Put them in the correct order of size starting with the biggest. Rub in the boxes to find the answer.

| A | GOLIATH | B | TREE | C | DAVID |

| D | SHEEP | E | MOUNTAIN | F | SOLDIER |

Your answer

Rub

David said he would fight the giant. Everyone laughed. 'You are just a young shepherd lad! Go back and look after your sheep!' they mocked him.

'I have killed many wild animals' said David. 'I have killed them with my own hands whenever they have attacked my sheep!'

What sort of wild animals might David have killed? See if you can guess from the clues in the little boxes before rubbing with your pencil.

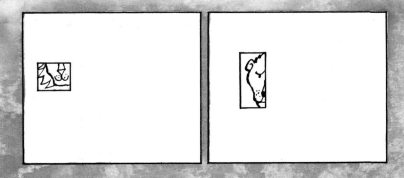

After trying to persuade the soldiers to let him fight Goliath, at last King Saul gave in and said that David could have a try.

Where is the king? Rub to put him on his throne.

There are six crowns hidden in this picture (as well as one of the shepherd's crooks).

Join up the dots to find out what King Saul gave to David.

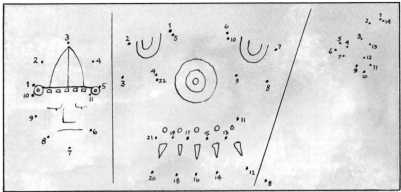

He gave David a bronze helmet and a coat of armour and his own sword. When David got them all on he could hardly walk straight. 'I cannot fight Goliath with all this on. It is much too heavy!'

Where is David? Rub above to find him.

He took the armour off and went out to fight Goliath with just two things...

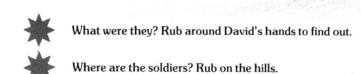

What were they? Rub around David's hands to find out.

Where are the soldiers? Rub on the hills.

What is David doing? Rub around his feet and hands to find out.

He chose five smooth stones from a stream and put them in his bag.

Goliath roared out, 'Do you take me for a dog, coming at me with that little stick! I am going to kill you, boy!'

Join the dots to draw your picture of Goliath.

'Not so!' said David. 'You have got fine weapons but God is on my side. I am going to defeat you!'

What weapons did Goliath have? Rub in the box to see if you are right.

Who was on David's side? Rub below.

David ran towards Goliath. He took one of the smooth stones and put it in his sling. Spinning the sling around his head he hurled the stone straight at the giant.

David's sling stone went straight to Goliath.
Find a crazy route for the stone.

Wham! The stone hit the fierce giant on the head and immediately killed him. The Philistines saw that their champion was dead and they . . . .

What did the soldiers do? Rub below to find out.

David had many other adventures. He did become king and he was a very wise ruler. He was the greatest king that Israel ever had.

He loved music and singing. Many of his poems are in the book of Psalms.

THIS STORY IS FOUND IN I SAMUEL
Chapters 16–17

From the clue in the box guess what David is playing then rub over the throne to find the rest of it and also to find King David himself.

 Did you find the ten shepherds' crooks?

Little Fish Surprise Picture Books

Just rub over the many Surprise areas with your soft pencil and see the pictures and puzzles appear!

Have lots of fun!

IN

NOAH'S BIG BOAT

JOSEPH AND HIS DREAMS

DAVID THE SHEPHERD BOY

CHRISTMAS IN BETHLEHEM

WISE MEN FIND JESUS

THE LITTLE MAN'S HAPPY DAY

THE GREAT BIG PICNIC

THE FIRST EASTER

5608703
USA ISBN 0-8307-1131-7
UK ISBN 0-948902-32-9